Short Stories on Character

The Bible Tells Me So Press

Short Stories on Character
Book 10

A children's book produced by
The Bible Tells Me So Press

PUBLISHED BY
THE BIBLE TELLS ME SO CORPORATION
WWW.THEBIBLETELLSMESO.COM

First Edition, September 2022

TABLE OF CONTENTS

BOOK 10   STORY 1
I Got This!

CLEAR

To be clear means to understand yourself and your limitations.
A clear person knows himself as well as others, and is able
to accept the fact that he can't excel in everything.

The school bell rang sharply signaling it was time for recess.

"Finally!" thought Sarah, as she and a large group of kids dashed out to the playground. Thirty minutes of soccer was Sarah's favorite thing to do during recess, and she didn't want to miss out for one minute. But there was a new girl in class named Rachel, who loved playing soccer too. Her problem was, she always hogged the ball and never passed it to anyone.

On this day, the two teams sprinted back and forth for 25 minutes, but neither side had scored. Rachel took a shot at the goal every time she got the ball and never gave anyone else a chance.

"There's only five minutes left in recess!" one of the girls called out. "So let's decide the game by taking some penalty shots. The first team to score, wins!"

"Great idea!" agreed Rachel. "I'll kick for us! Don't worry, guys. I got this!" But when Rachel took her shot, it rolled slowly on the ground, straight into the goalie's hands. Now it was time for the other team to kick. Sarah asked her team, "Who do you all think is the best one to put in the goal for our team?" Rachel jumped up, "Oh, that's me! No question about it! It's a good thing you guys have me on your team. And don't worry, I got this!"

Before anyone could say a word, Rachel had already taken her position as the goalie and told the other team to go ahead and take their kick. Sarah and the rest of her teammates looked on nervously, barely able to watch. Would Rachel be able to stop the shot, or would the other team score on their first penalty kick and win the game?

The kicker for the other team was Ricky. He positioned himself near the center of the field and stood there looking right at Rachel for a moment. Sarah felt a dull ache in her stomach because she knew Ricky was very strong and could kick the ball super hard. He sprinted forward, planted his left foot, and swung his right foot around to kick the ball. Whoosh! Just as Sarah feared, it flew right over Rachel and into the goal. Rachel jumped for the ball, but it was too late. The ball was already sitting on the ground in the back of the net. The other team cheered and clapped, while Sarah's face was flushed completely red. She was annoyed because Rachel thought she was so good at everything.

When Sarah got home that afternoon, she was still bothered about it. Her mom noticed it right away when she shuffled in the door and closed it loudly. "Is everything okay, Sarah?" she asked. Sarah responded, "Ugh, no. There's this new girl in my class named Rachel. She thinks she's the best at everything. Whenever we play soccer, she always shoots it and never passes the ball. And today we lost the game because of her." By now, Sarah had slumped down on the couch, and her mother came over to her side. She sat quietly, while Sarah rubbed her face in her hands.

"Oh my!" sighed Mom after a few moments. "It seems like Rachel needs to learn that no one can do everything." Sarah looked up into her mother's eyes, as her mother continued. "You know, we all really need others. Some people are good at certain things, while others are good at something else. I know for a fact that I need you kids and Dad."

"Really?" replied Sarah, surprised. "Yes," Mom answered. "We need to understand our limitations and then work together. You have to be clear about yourself and your strengths and weaknesses.

This is not a sad thing. It's an encouraging thing. When we understand our own limitations and let others shine, it makes everyone much happier." Sarah responded, "Thanks, Mom. I'll try to talk to her and see what I can do tomorrow."

The next day at recess, they all headed to the field again. Sarah was a little nervous as she thought about what to say to Rachel. Once again, when they started to play, Rachel wouldn't pass the ball and missed a couple of easy shots. By the time recess was almost over, the game was in a tie just like the day before.

"Should we do penalty kicks again to choose the winner?" Joey asked. Rachel joined in, "Yes! And I want to be the goalie again! Don't worry. I got this." Sarah summoned up the courage and responded, "Maybe we can let someone else try. How about Joseph? He's tall, and he's got a great reach when he dives for the ball. How about we let Joseph be the goalie on this one?"

After struggling for a few minutes, Rachel reluctantly agreed. She remembered how she missed the ball the day before. The others turned to Joseph and asked what he thought. He responded, "I don't know. Do you think I can do it?" The whole team smiled at him and said, "Don't worry, Joseph. You got this." Joseph walked over to the goal. When the other team kicked the ball, Joseph leaped up and blocked it just in time. A few moments later, Rachel asked Sarah to take the next kick. Sarah made the shot and they won! Everyone was happy, but Rachel was happiest of all.

Bible Verse

Not regarding each his own virtues, but each the virtues of others also.

Philippians 2:4

Family Talk Time!

In this story there was a new girl at Sarah's school named Rachel. She thought she was the best soccer player. At first, Rachel was not a team player. She was not clear that she wasn't the best at everything. After losing a game, her teammates stepped in to help her understand that she couldn't excel in everything. She needed to give others, who were better than her, the opportunity to play. In the end, Rachel was able to accept the fact that Joseph could do a better job of playing goalie than she could. We need to be clear. It is not easy to know ourselves and understand our limitations. We need to recognize that others may be better than us at a particular thing and let them do it.

Things to consider...

1. What important lesson did Rachel learn in this story?

2. How did Sarah's talk with her mom help her?

3. Have you ever gotten clear about something that you didn't realize about yourself?

BOOK 10   STORY 2

Two Sandwiches

MAGNANIMOUS

To be magnanimous means to be generous or forgiving, especially toward a rival. A magnanimous person is not cruel, but tolerates others and treats them kindly.

Ezra kept looking at the clock. He was getting really hungry. He was looking forward to the turkey sandwich his mom had made him. She always made it just right with mayonnaise and mustard and lots of pickles. Finally the bell rang, and the class scurried to the cafeteria. Ezra grabbed his lunch off the lunch cart and met his friend Jeremy at the table by the window. With his stomach growling, he could finally get everything out of the bag. Ezra sighed happily as he dug into the baby carrots.

But out of nowhere, one kid from another class passed by and grabbed his sandwich. Before Ezra could say anything, the boy turned and quickly walked away, eating the sandwich as he went. For a moment, Ezra just sat there shocked. "Did you see that?" Ezra asked Jeremy in disbelief. "He just took my sandwich! Who is he? Do you know him?"

"Yes, I know him," Jeremy replied. "He is a grade older than us. I've seen him before playing basketball outside. He lives near me." Ezra's eyes were wide open, and he stammered, "What do I do now? Look! My sandwich is all gone. He ate the whole thing." Fortunately, Jeremy acted quickly and decided to split his sandwich with him. "Here, have this. You can have some of my crackers too." Ezra felt numb with disappointment for the rest of the day, but was glad Jeremy had helped him.

The next day, Ezra made a plan. He would sit by himself and keep a close eye on his food. He was halfway through lunch, and everything was going well. But soon he got thirsty and went to get some water. He was just gone for a minute or two. When he returned, to his dismay, his sandwich was gone again!

Ezra looked around in a panic. Sure enough, a few tables over, sat

the same boy munching down the last bite of Ezra's sandwich. "What?" Ezra exclaimed under his breath. "This can't be happening again. I wanted my sandwich!" He was very upset this time, and even worse, Jeremy wasn't there to help him out. Ezra went back to class very hungry. And he kept thinking about what to do tomorrow. By the end of the day, he had decided to talk to his parents about it.

Ezra burst into the kitchen where his mother was slicing apples. "Mom, I need a big snack. I didn't get to eat my sandwich today. And I didn't get to eat it yesterday." His mother paused for a moment, puzzled by this announcement. "What do you mean, Ezra? Your lunch was packed just like you like it." She set a plate of apple slices down for Ezra, and he wolfed them down hungrily. "An older kid at my school has taken my sandwich the last couple of days. I don't know what to do. He is bigger than me, and I'm afraid to say anything to him. But what if this happens again tomorrow? If I don't say anything, he might keep taking it and eating it."

Ezra looked up at his mother and noticed her color flashed, and her mouth dropped open with a stern look. "Ezra..." she started, but then trailed off. Ezra continued eating apples. But his heart felt very heavy, and the kitchen fell very quiet. A few minutes passed as Mom looked out the window. "Son," she finally said, softly this time. "What about this idea? Tomorrow I'll make two sandwiches. One for you and one for him. Look for him at lunch, offer him the second sandwich, and see what happens."

Ezra stopped eating and looked again at his mother, surprised, "Are you serious? Give him a sandwich after he kept taking mine? Why would I do that?" Mom responded, "Maybe there is more going

on here than we know." Ezra hesitated and then said, "Okay, I'll try to do that."

The next day at lunch, Ezra pulled out both sandwiches and scanned the room. Sure enough, there he was! Ezra slowly walked up to him, clutching the extra sandwich. "Hello there. I just wanted to give you this. It really bothered me what you did. So today I brought an extra one for you." The other boy was completely lost for what to say, and immediately sat down and started tearing up. After an awkward moment, he turned to Ezra. "I'm really sorry. I know I shouldn't have done that. The last couple of days, my lunch has gone missing from the lunch cart, and I don't know why. I have diabetes, and I get really sick if I don't eat my meals on time, so I was desperate to eat something." Now, Ezra was the one who was surprised. "Oh no!" he replied. "I didn't know that was the reason. Come on. Let's talk to your teacher about your missing lunch."

As soon as Ezra got home, his mom asked, "How did it go today at lunch?" "Oh Mom!" he exclaimed, the words tumbling out all at once. "You wouldn't believe it. His lunch had gone missing. And he had to eat or he would get sick! That's why he was taking my sandwiches. And the teacher figured out he was putting his lunch on the wrong cart." Ezra's mom beamed. "Incredible! I'm so impressed how you took care of him like that. It would have been easy to be harsh. But instead, you were generous and forgiving. There is a word for this—it's called magnanimous. This boy wronged you, but you chose to treat him kindly and cared for him with such a big heart." Ezra grinned and hugged his mom. "Thanks, Mom. That was a great idea." And his heart swelled and felt much bigger indeed.

Bible Verse

If your enemy is hungry, give him bread to eat; and if he is thirsty, give him water to drink.

Proverbs 25:21

Family Talk Time!

In this story Ezra is being challenged by a boy who is taking his sandwiches two days in a row. After talking to his mom about these incidents at school, Ezra follows her advice, brings this boy a sandwich, and talks to him about what is going on. He is not cruel to him but forgives him and shows generosity. It is not always easy to treat someone who hurts us or is unkind to us with magnanimity, but Ezra is able to do this rather than reacting and treating him harshly. This week find an opportunity to be magnanimous to someone who may not treat you very well.

Things to consider...

1. How was Ezra magnanimous in this story? Did he react cruelly when he was wronged by someone?

2. Have you ever given someone more than they expected or deserved? How did that feel?

3. How can you practice developing the trait of being magnanimous?

BOOK 10   STORY 3

A False Alarm

SERIOUS

To be serious is not to be playful or joking around. A serious person's actions carry weight and importance due to his proper character.

The weekend Ezra was waiting for was finally here. A few of his friends and their dads had planned an outing together. They were going camping for two nights in the woods, and there would be hiking in the hill country, fishing in a creek, and roasting marshmallows over a fire.

All the boys were brimming with excitement. That made the drive seem quick, and before they knew it, they had pulled up to the campground. Everyone piled out and started unloading all their gear. "Oh no!" cried Steven suddenly. "I just realized I forgot my sleeping bag at home. I guess I'll have to just sleep in the dirt."

Everyone stopped, and Ezra was most alarmed of all. "That's going to hurt, Steven. The ground is so hard. Maybe we can all give him one of our extra blankets that he could make into a bed." Right away everyone responded positively and started digging through their packs. "Yes, we can do that for our friend," they said.

Steven stood there watching with a sly grin. Then he burst into laughter, "Ha, Ha. Gotcha. Here's my sleeping bag right here." The others groaned, "Here we go again, another one of Steven's tricks." Steven was a jokester and loved playing tricks on them. With a low grumble, everyone returned to finish unloading the cars and setting up the tents.

Somehow, Steven and his dad finished their tent first, so Steven headed toward the woods to do a little exploring. But after a few minutes, he rushed back into the camp screaming and hollering. "Everybody, come see! There's a giant lizard sleeping all curled up in a tree. You have to come see this!"

The boys all dropped what they were doing and ran over to Steven. "Where is it? We want to see!" they all exclaimed at once. And before anyone could stop them, everyone scampered after Steven down the trail and out of sight.

They followed the trail past a large thicket of brush, and when they turned the corner right behind it, they saw only one thing. There was Steven, bent over double and laughing at all of them. "Ha! My trick worked! You guys would believe anything. No lizard here, sorry." This time Mark reacted, "That's not funny, Steven. Can you be serious for once and not just joke and trick us all the time?" "Where's the fun in that?" Steven replied. Tired and dejected, the boys trudged back to the campground. The rest of the evening was spent around the campfire roasting hot dogs and marshmallows. Later, they listened to stories from their dads until falling asleep.

The next morning, everyone ran about preparing for the day's activities. Some of the boys would go fishing, but Ezra, Steven, and Mark chose hiking since there weren't enough fishing poles for everyone. "Watch out on the way back down! The trail is very rough!" Mark's dad called out as the boys headed off into the woods. They were interested in picking berries that were growing in that area. Right away, Mark spotted some bright red berries in the distance and started running up the trail. Suddenly, he tripped over a tree root in the path and lay sprawled out on the ground in pain. "My foot!" cried Mark as the other boys reached him. "I can't get up. It really hurts." Ezra knelt down beside him. "Oh no! What should we do? Steven, can you run back and get some help? Mark can't walk. I'll stay with him and wait."

Steven dashed to the creek where the others were fishing. He was

sweating, and his face was red with despair. He shouted, "Mark's hurt! We need help! Everyone, please come quickly!" The others looked back at him and then to each other. "Very funny, Steven. You can't fool us this time. I'm about to catch a fish. They're biting today," one of the boys responded. "Yeah, try your tricks on somebody else. It won't work with us," said another.

Steven stood still, shocked at the situation. He was desperate to help Mark, but now no one believed him. His previous tricks caused them to not take him seriously. In a panic, he turned and ran back to Ezra and Mark and told them what happened. "Ezra, you better go and tell them. They will believe you." "Hurry!" cried Mark, as Ezra nodded and headed back. As soon as he reached his friends and told them what had happened, everyone believed him right away. Mark's dad grabbed the first aid kit and asked Ezra to lead the way. Mark was still in pain, and by the time they got back, his ankle was swollen. His dad wrapped it up and helped him get back to the camp.

That night while they sat around the campfire, everyone was quiet. Steven finally interrupted the silence and spoke up, "I'd like to say something about today. I'm really sorry, everyone. I was joking around too much, and that made Mark hurt more." After a few quiet moments, Ezra's dad responded, "Thank you, Steven. We really are proud of all you boys. There will be joking now and then, but be careful. Otherwise it becomes who we are, and when that happens, it's hard for people to take us seriously." Everyone nodded in agreement, and Ezra leaned back on his father's side, grateful for that moment together they would never forget.

Bible Verse

Let no one despise your youth, but be a pattern to the believers in word, in conduct, in love, in faith, in purity.

1 Timothy 4:12

Family Talk Time!

In this story Ezra and Mark and a few of their friends go camping. Steven likes to play tricks on everyone and joke around. As a result, no one believes him when he says Mark is hurt and needs help. We should be careful about joking around too much, so it does not become who we are. When you are young, you can learn how to behave and speak with the discretion needed to be a serious person.

Things to consider...

1. What kind of person was Steven?

2. Why do you think no one believed Steven when he tried to get help for Mark?

3. Why did everyone believe Ezra right away?

4. Can you think of a time when you had to be serious? Did others take you seriously?